ooh la la!

perfect hair

ooh la la!
perfect hair

Susie Galvez

Illustrated by Chico Hayasaki

MQP

Published by MQ Publications Limited
12 The Ivories
6–8 Northampton Street
London, N1 2HY
email: mail@mqpublications.com
website: www.mqpublications.com

Illustrator: Chico Hayasaki/www.cwc-i.com
Editor: Laura Kesner
Senior Designer: Victoria Bevan

ISBN: 1-84072-591-5
10 9 8 7 6 5 4 3 2 1

This book is intended as an informational guide only and is not to be used as a substitute
for professional medical care or treatment. Neither the author nor the publisher can be
held responsible for any damage, injury, or otherwise resulting from the use of the
information in this book.

Printed and bound in France by *Partenaires-Livres*® (JL)

Contents

Introduction 7

Color cues 8

Maintaining the mane 26

Remedies 46

Tricks of the trade 66

Styling 86

About the author 108

Special appreciation 111

Introduction

In search of the perfect hairdo, but don't know what to do or how to do it? You've come to the perfect place.

Ooh La La! Perfect Hair detangles the mysteries that lie behind great looking hair and provides you with all the information you need to groom your mane to glory.

Discover the secrets to perfect coloring and styling. Unravel remedies for any hair condition or situation that may occur, and learn tactics for avoiding those dreaded "bad hair days." Take a peek behind the scenes and pick up tricks and techniques from top stylists that will make your hair look salon-perfect.

Enough hair-teasing. It's time to dust off your hairbrush and closely examine all the secrets that lie within *Ooh La La! Perfect Hair*.

Get the combs and conditioner at the ready—Let's go!

Chapter 1

Color cues

Don't cross the line

If you are giving your hair an overall color or body wave, add a line of petroleum jelly along the hairline before beginning the process. The petroleum jelly forms a barrier, keeping the color or perm solution off the delicate skin at the hairline. Rinse it off when you have completed the process. Hair color will be perfect, skin is saved from color skid marks, and the strong chemicals of the permanent solution are kept far away from your delicate facial skin.

Don't fade away

Highlighting or color enhancing shampoos are designed to help preserve your hair color. They keep your color from fading and can replace lost color tone. In addition to adding extra shine and reducing brassiness, highlighting or color enhancing shampoos will help extend the life of your color. To avoid adding too much color, alternate the shampoo designed for treated hair with your regular shampoo.

Not so dumb

Blondes have about 140,000 hairs on the head. This is the most of any hair color count. Brunettes average 100,000, and redheads about 90,000. The reason is unclear, but for those without abundant blonde tresses, take comfort in knowing that blonde hair is typically finer, making it harder to hold a style. While the jury is still out on whether "blondes have more fun," there's no doubt that their finer hair usually requires more hair styling time.

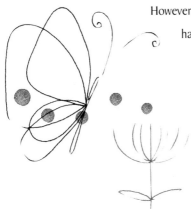

However, nowadays no one with fine, limp hair has to suffer. The current trend in hair styling products includes thickeners, which help add body to fine hair, creating the illusion of more voluminous hair. Be sure to ask your stylist which products will work best on your type of hair, be it fine, thick, or curly.

Sunny side up

Colored and permed hair needs to be protected from the sun. Before going outside in the summer months, dab a tiny bit of conditioner over the surface of the hair. This will keep the hair from drying out or lightening up. A hat provides the best protection from damaging rays. If swimming, comb a bit of conditioner through the hair beforehand to help stop it absorbing the pool's chemicals.

Lighten up

Beginning at about the age of 25 years old, we sometimes begin to lose pigment in our skin, eyes, and hair, which gives us a softer, lighter look. If you notice that this is happening to your coloring, try keeping hair color on the lighter side, especially around the face. Do not, however, try to exactly match the color of hair you enjoyed when you were young—the contrast can be too severe and the look will scream harsh and fake. Opt instead for highlighting the hair.

Wig out!

If you are trying to decide whether to color your hair, first try on a wig to see if the color suits you. Fiery-red hair or raven-black tresses may be what you picture in your mind's eye, but they may create quite a different impression when you finally see yourself up close and in person.

Trying on wigs offers a fun, free, and fail-safe way to explore hair color before taking the plunge. Who knows, you may find out that you suit more than one color. Choose a shade and wig out!

Great tip

Hair painting is a process in which color is brushed on to the hair's surface using a special paintbrush type tool. It is perfect for bangs since you can add color along the soft edges and catch the light with your chosen color. This technique is also called color tipping.

Tip tips

The hair tips are much more porous than the rest of the hair shaft, causing them to absorb more hair color than any other area. To keep color even, apply a conditioner to the ends of the hair while the roots are processing. During the last five to seven minutes, comb the color over the entire hair shaft including the conditioned tips. The conditioner will keep the color from going on too heavily, and allow for an even, all-over hair color.

Trendy tresses

Hair color takes its cues from runways in Paris, London, and Milan. In style now are hair color "fashions," a combination of several beautiful colors gently blended through one head of hair. The colors create interesting contrasts and contours that shape a cut, illuminate the eyes, show off a facial shape, and allow the wearer's true personality to shine. The trend of strategically placed highlights accentuates the hair's surface layers, while the inner sections of hair glow with rich, deep color shadows to add depth and dimension.

Also on the fashion front are solid, one-color looks among the young or young at heart. Although one color can border on boring, the new depth and richness of available colors transcend the boring and create the beautiful. With today's coloring options, changing your hair color is as easy as changing your mind!

Frosting is for cakes

Frosting is a technique in which the hair is pulled through a plastic cap with a crochet-type hook. The result is all over bleached color intertwined with your natural color hair. Although it is often a cheaper option, it can be an uncomfortable process, and the results are very aging to the face, as hair usually turns out the color of salt and pepper. Be sure to streak or paint your hair for a modern and glossy finish—without the "ouch" factor.

Root canal

When roots suddenly appear and you have no time to color, a sure fire camouflage is to zigzag your hair's part. The back and forth movement of the part makes the root re-growth less noticeable. A hair mascara also works wonders—just color the offending area with a close-matching colored hair mascara. Sometimes root showings can be a bit sexy. Other times roots look like a runway landing strip for airplanes. Re-color soon!

High and low

Highlights look terrific on almost everyone. So why isn't everyone highlighting? Usually, it is the cost that holds us back. To add the lightness that highlighting brings, try this easy, low-cost way to add a little bit of zip to your hair with—believe it or not—flavored vinegars. Just choose a flavor for your hair's highlights.

✳ Light blondes: use white vinegar.

✳ Darker blondes: use balsamic vinegar.

✳ Brunettes: use red wine vinegar.

✳ Redheads: use raspberry flavored vinegar.

Mix six tablespoons of vinegar into your shampoo and leave on for 15 minutes. Rinse thoroughly. The vinegar will not only enhance highlights but also give hair a super-shiny finish.

The lighter side

Color the section of hair that frames your face a shade or two lighter than the rest of your hair. This helps avoid the harshness of a "dyed" hair look and brightens the face, giving it more glow and radiance.

Fashion statement

Unless you are making a serious fashion statement, hair color should look natural. The ideal color is two to three shades lighter or darker than Mother Nature intended.

To test the waters of hair color, try adding a few highlights or lowlights where permanent color is applied to only certain strands of hair, to either darken or lighten the look. You will get the effects of colored hair without a lot of time or cost.

On the mark

Cream hair colors are easier to apply than the liquid kind. Creams stay where applied, without dripping. As an added bonus, their pH level is usually lower, which is kinder to the hair shaft. If given the choice, always choose the cream for less mess and beautiful color.

Take it away

If you are new to home-coloring your hair, start with a temporary color. Temporary color washes out in about six to eight shampoos. You will get the look and feel of what coloring is about without the dreaded permanent color foul-ups. We have all heard about the tinge of green, or the dreadful pumpkin orange when "baby's breath blonde" was what was envisioned! The models on hair color kits always have beautiful hair and the directions read as easy as a-b-c, but a cheap home hair-color kit could cost you an expensive trip to the salon. With a temporary color, at worst, you will spend the night washing and re-washing until the color has faded or gone.

Pick-me-up

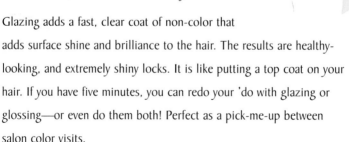

For a fast hair rejuvenation, try glossing or glazing. Glossing is a five-minute "refresher" of permanent hair color and conditioner. A quick application of hair color is applied all over the hair. After five minutes the hair is rinsed and styled as usual. The effects are brighter color, maximum shine, and, in most cases, the hair has more body.

Glazing adds a fast, clear coat of non-color that adds surface shine and brilliance to the hair. The results are healthy-looking, and extremely shiny locks. It is like putting a top coat on your hair. If you have five minutes, you can redo your 'do with glazing or glossing—or even do them both! Perfect as a pick-me-up between salon color visits.

Hair speak

With the growth in popularity of hair coloring, it is time to update our hair color terminology.

* Dying is something we used to do—now we call it "color treating."

* A makeover is now "modernizing."

* Bleach is for clothes—we now "lighten" our hair.

* Roots are old news—we now have "apparent re-growth."

* Hair color has become "hair cosmetic."

* Double-processing is out, "two-shade color" is in.

* Covering the gray is now referred to as "natural blending."

* Streaks are old—"highlights" are new.

Fashion forward

Image experts suggest that along with updating your wardrobe, you should update your hair color and cut to keep fresh and current. Any type of hair can be highlighted. Thin hair will look thicker and fuller; thick hair will have more movement and depth.

Streaks are best when done in several different shades of the same color family. Two or three different shades of blonde can be used on lighter hair, and red, honey, or bronze streaks are breathtaking on redheads or brunettes.

Color time line

Semi-permanent hair color should be refreshed every four to six shampoos. Permanent all-over color needs to be touched up about every four weeks. Highlights, the workhorse of coloring applications, need refreshing only four to six times a year. Highlight shampoos, glosses, and glazes can keep colored tresses lasting even longer. Ask your stylist which color-extending product will work best for your hair.

Chapter 2

Maintaining the mane

All wrapped up

Enjoy a spa hair-conditioning treatment anytime you want smoother, more lustrous locks. Simply apply a deep-penetrating conditioner to the hair, comb through, and wrap hair in plastic wrap. Cover with a warm, moist towel and then put a large shower cap over the towel to hold in the warm moisture. Allow the conditioner to penetrate for 20 minutes then rinse thoroughly. Towel dry and if possible, allow the hair to dry naturally so as not to pull out the just-added deep conditioning.

Beauty brew

Tea and beer rinses improve the look of the hair and are so easy to do. Begin by boiling two servings of tea leaves—either loose or by opening two tea bags and placing the contents in the pot. Strain the leaves from the liquid and allow it to cool. Put into a container that allows for easy pouring. Apply to the hair as a rinse after 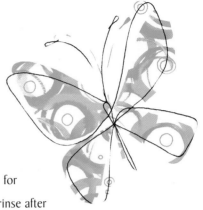 shampooing and gently comb the tea through the hair for a minute or two. Rinse lightly and then style your hair as normal. Beer also gives the hair body and makes it more manageable. Pour a bottle of beer over the hair, working it in with the fingers for a couple of minutes. Rinse well and style as usual. You will notice that both the tea and the beer will give your hair a lot more shine, bounce, and body. Make mine a cup of shine!

Such a tease

Fine hair is destined to droop naturally over the course of the day, or because of the weather, or both. Maybe a little teasing is what your hair needs. What started in the '60s is back—and has always been in vogue for fine-haired gals.

To add a bit of lift to your super-fine locks, hold a section of hair gently between the finger and the thumb, allowing for some hair to escape. Just at the roots, lightly tease a couple of times using a brush with flexible bristles. Be gentle and don't pull at the hair. Then turn your head upside down and spray the roots lightly with hairspray and style as usual. Your style will now stay in place all day!

Bye-bye dry

If your hair looks dull or frizzy, has split ends galore, is stiff and hard to style, or breaks off easily, try a moisturizing shampoo as well as a deep conditioner (one that is left on for at least five minutes). Plan an even deeper hair treatment at least twice a month to really condition and hydrate the hair shaft and scalp. Choose hair color in the most moisturizing formula available that is made without alcohol.

Once is always enough

Ignore the words "lather, rinse, repeat" on shampoo bottles. Salons will lather up twice because it feels so great to the scalp. Lathering or shampooing hair once is enough 99 percent of the time. The other one percent, when you need to lather up twice, is for those ultra heavy-duty mud packs or cream packs, when your hair still feels heavy or limp with product. Even when a second lathering is necessary, make it on the light side.

Cheers!

Rinsing hair with champagne brings out blonde highlights. Conditioning the hair with another raise-your-glass beverage, beer, adds a lot of shine to your tresses. So the next time you indulge, save a little "cheer" for your hair.

Too much of a good thing

In centuries past, hair was washed on average once a week. Now with conveniences such as blow-dryers, curling irons, diffusers, and crimpers, we wash and change our hair more often than we change our minds! This excessive washing is extremely taxing on the hair and scalp—no matter how gentle the product used. If you must shampoo often, use only the kindest, most gentle products that you can find. Shampoo very lightly, lathering only once. Condition only when necessary to avoid buildup and use a water-soluble styling product.

Royal treatment

Cleopatra kept her tresses flowing with this simple hair treatment. Combine ¹/₂ cup of honey with two tablespoons of olive oil. Mix well. Work into the scalp and down through the hair all the way to the ends. Using a wide-tooth comb gently work the honey/olive oil mixture through your hair. Next, cover hair with a plastic shower cap and allow the treatment to work for 30 minutes. For an extra beauty benefit, place a towel in the microwave for a few moments and then surround the plastic cap with the warm towel to help the treatment penetrate even deeper. Shampoo out, rinse well, and pat dry. Hair will be silky, smooth, and luxuriously shiny—there's no de-Nile.

Wave hello

If summer plans call for a dip in the sea, braid your hair in two or more braids before you take the plunge. Swim and have fun. As you walk along the shore, allow the sea breeze to dry your hair. After drying, take out the braids, and run your fingers through the wonderful waves Mother Nature has given you. Easy, breezy, wavy, summer hair.

Tropical topic

For a deep-down hair conditioner with the exotic flavor of the islands, put $^1/_4$ cup of rum and two eggs in a pourable container and mix well. Shampoo as usual. Rinse the hair, then pour the tropical mixture over it. Comb the deep conditioner through and cover hair with a disposable plastic shower cap. Allow to work for five to seven minutes. Rinse thoroughly with cool water and pat dry. Afterward, hair will feel healthy and full of shine and movement.

Stop signs

Before cutting, follow these guidelines to find out how short you can attractively wear your hair:

✳ Look straight into the mirror.

✳ Use your finger to follow a line on your neck directly down from your earlobe. Stop when your finger is perfectly in line with the tip of your chin—or the lowest part of the chin (if you have a double chin).

✳ Measure the distance using a tape measure or ruler.

✳ If the distance is more than $2\frac{1}{4}$ inches—short hair will not be as flattering, so plan on a little extra length. You can still achieve a shorter, wispy style by adding layers at this level.

✳ If your distance is under $2\frac{1}{4}$ inches—a short 'do will most certainly do for you!

Tress caress

Washing the hair is something we do instinctively, but are we using shampoo to our best advantage? To keep hair at its healthiest, begin with water to open the hair cuticle. Allow the water to stream over the hair for at least two minutes before beginning the cleansing process. Depending on hair length, pour a coin-sized dollop of shampoo into hands. Rub hands together and begin to shampoo at the scalp. Massage the scalp with fingertips—never the fingernails. Rinse in cool water to help close the cuticle and stimulate the scalp. If daily conditioner is used, apply lightly and rinse hair thoroughly. Blot—don't rub—the hair dry with a big fluffy towel. Excess rubbing can damage the hair shaft causing split ends. If time permits, air dry the hair to give it a rest from the blow-dryer inferno. If no extra time is available, switch the dryer setting to "cool" toward the end of the drying time to help protect hair.

Back up plan

If you are washing and blow-drying your hair on a daily basis just to give your 'do that fresh feeling, you might be overdoing it. Unless the hair is super oily, most of us can get by with shampooing every other day.

To get that fresh 'do feeling on your off day, try a curling iron. First spritz hair with water, blow-dry for a few seconds, and then curl lightly with a curling iron. The size of the rod will determine the size of the curl. The best curling irons, like the professional types, have variable temperatures for different types of hair. Using the curling iron between shampoos will give you that fresh hair feeling while saving the hair from overexposure.

Take your time

In our daily dash to shower, shampoo, and condition, most of the time we do not shampoo long enough. Start by wetting the hair for at least one minute, then apply shampoo and massage into scalp and hair for another two minutes. Rinse, rinse, rinse. Apply conditioner if needed and wait for two minutes before rinsing out. Good hair products only do a great job for the hair if we do our part and use them correctly.

Scent-imental

For a bit of extra glam, add a spritz of your favorite signature fragrance onto your hairbrush and comb before styling. Also, a spritz of fragrance in the hair while putting on your hair mousse or gel will leave your hair lightly scented. As you move, your "essence" will go with you. This is a great idea if you tend to be fragrance sensitive, since the aroma will be light, yet pleasing.

Short stop

Hair will always lift about $^1/_2$ an inch shorter
when it is dry as opposed to when it is wet.
So if you want a chin-length bob cut,
you must have your hair cut about
$^1/_2$ an inch longer for it to be the
perfect chin length when it dries.
When cutting bangs, be careful
not to pull them taut when trimming,
as they will also lift up about $^1/_2$ an
inch when dry. The best way to trim
bangs is just to snip them as they
lay—better yet have a professional do
it. A lot of hair salons offer complimentary
bang trims between cuts—check yours out!

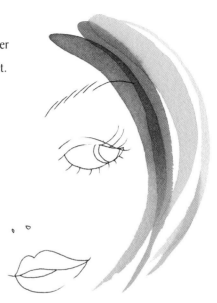

Plant it

Look for shampoo labels that feature plant extracts such as sweet almond oil, jojoba, avocado, tea tree oil, peppermint oil, carrot extract, lavender, rosemary, and wheat germ. Plant extracts buffer moisture loss and keep hair from drying while wheat germ adds body and coats the hair shaft, protecting it from breaking.

Don't pluck

Do not be tempted to pluck a gray hair from your head. Pulling out the gray hair will not kill the hair or make it grow back in your original color. Plucking will only distort the hair follicle, making the re-growth more wiry and obvious. Save the plucking for the eyebrows!

Pay at the pump

Volumizing and body-building shampoos contain proteins that bind to the hair shaft and add volume and fullness to the hair. If hair is fine or tends to go flat, try a volumizing shampoo to pump up the volume. Since these products are designed to add volume and weight to the hair, they contain more ingredients such as protein, which is an excellent body builder, but can build up and over-coat the hair if used too often. It is best to use your regular shampoo and conditioner every third or fourth wash to help keep the buildup to a minimum, or invest in a clarifying shampoo that will cleanse the hair and remove any impurities.

In style

Whatever your hair length—super-short or waist-length tresses—regular trims every six to eight weeks are the key to keeping hair healthy. Each hair shaft grows at its own speed. Snipping off the dry ends on a regular basis prevents the hair from splitting and allows healthy nutrients from hair products to penetrate all the way from the scalp to the hair's tip as well as keeping your style…in style!

Don't stop

The next time you visit your hairstylist, ask the shampoo technician to spend extra time performing a scalp massage. Most technicians are happy to oblige. The extra massage of the scalp and back of the neck will do wonders for your mood. Excess tension and stress will simply drain away from your head and neck. Make sure that you tip him or her appropriately for a job well done.

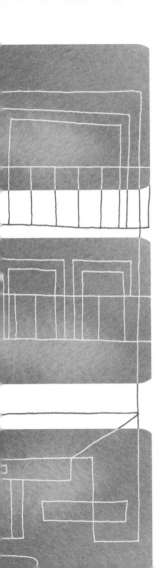

Chapter 3

Remedies

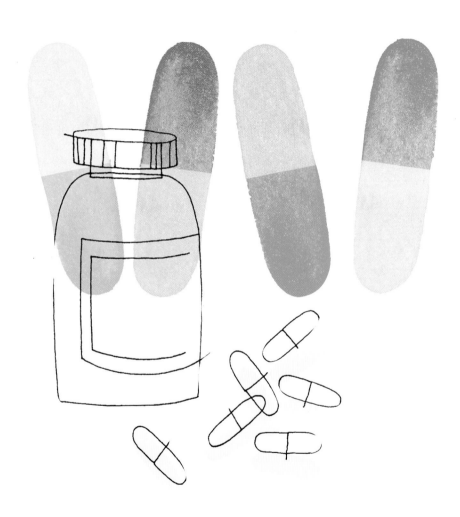

Heads up

Dandruff remedies focus on putting products "on" the scalp to alleviate the condition, usually with minimal results. One only has to wear dark colored clothes to see, first hand, if the treatment is working or not. Why not try inward thinking instead?

Vitamins and supplements work from the inside out. Zinc lozenges, vitamin B6, vitamin B complex, vitamin E, kelp tablets, omega 3 fatty acids, and evening primrose oil offer relief for dry, itchy scalps. Beta-carotene, vitamin A, and lecithin are also found to be helpful in diminishing the symptoms by adding strength to the cells of the hair and the scalp. Some vitamin companies are making vitamin and mineral supplements designed solely to improve the hair. Others offer products for hair, nails, and skin. Ask if your pharmacy offers them.

For even better results combine the healthy hair inward program with a topical hair-care product designed to help reduce the amount of flakes.

Stop the madness

Too much shampoo and conditioner can leave a buildup of residue on the hair leaving it flat and dull. Here's where a never-ending no-win cycle of hair care can start. To remove residue, you could use a clarifying shampoo. However, these can sometimes over-strip the hair, leaving it flat and flyaway. To compensate, you could add a silicone product to make your hair shine again. But this may over-coat your hair and make it look limp and lifeless. So you are back where you began and start the maddening cycle all over again. To break the chain, use only gentle products designed for your hair type and condition and try to use them sparingly.

Lighten the load

If your hair is overloaded with styling products and no clarifying shampoo is available, try this quick fix. Add one tablespoon of baking soda to your usual application of shampoo. Mix well in your hands, lather up as usual, rinse, and follow with your conditioner, if needed. Baking soda is a heavy-duty cleanser, and it also helps to seal the hair cuticle, protecting it and leaving the hair shiny.

Cut it out

If you have just received a haircut that you absolutely hate, wait a bit before you rush off at a mad pace to get it fixed. Try to wait at least one week. By being patient you will have time to evaluate it, practice styling it, and maybe even decide to like it. Often, a positive response from other people could change your mind. If you still hate it after a week, then at least your re-cutting decision will be rational. And perhaps you will have had time to find a photo of the hairstyle you thought you were getting in the first place!

Shine on

The secret to shiny hair is to rinse hair thoroughly. A tried and true shiny hair rinse is to mix a tablespoon of vinegar or lemon juice into a glass of cool water and stir well. Gently pour the mixture over the hair then rinse with cool water. The acidic treatment closes the hair cuticle, and gives hair a glossy shine.

Clarify the situation

Clarifying shampoo is a deeply cleansing solution designed to remove the buildup of styling products, over-conditioning, and excess oils. Although clarifying shampoos are much too drying to use on a daily basis, they are excellent to "spring clean" the hair. If you use a clarifying shampoo before you color, perm, or relax your hair, the processing products penetrate better and spread more evenly over the hair, as the hair shaft is free of coating.

Oil well

If hair tends to look greasy, clumps together at the roots, or gets dirty all too quickly, frequent shampooing is necessary. Choose a gentle "for daily use" shampoo and rinse hair well. Excessive oiliness may by caused by genetics, sweating (as in exercising), or lack of essential vitamins. Even stress can add to the overall oil production. To take control of the excess oil eat healthily, get the proper amount of sleep, and de-stress as much as possible.

All for one

While a shampoo and conditioner built into one product may sound like a dream come true, it may actually be a nightmare for hair. As a rule, the all-in-one products tend to build up very quickly on the hair shaft causing the hair to be flat and dull. Oily hair? Don't even think about it. Your hair will look the same after washing as it did before you started—yuk!

Fly stand by

Both dry and moist air can make the hair look like it is about to take off. To help keep dry, flyaway hair under control, try spraying a static-out product (made for clothes) onto your hairbrush before using. Spraying the brush lightly with hairspray can also work. As for the frizz caused by humid weather—lightly mist the hair all over with mineral water. Work a tiny dot of leave-in conditioner through the hair, all the way to the ends. Style as usual and then let the hair dry—in place. Frizzies will be gone and hair will both look and feel sleek, shiny, and tamed.

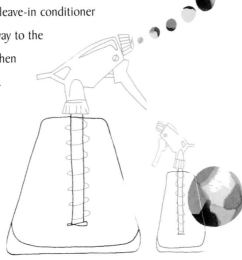

Headliners

For really bad hair days when nothing, but nothing, will work, decide not to fight it. Instead simply pull your hair back using a wet comb. Add a little dab of conditioner to give your hair a bit of a beauty treatment—despite its refusal to behave! Pick out a headband in your favorite color or material and use it to hold your hair back off your face. Your style now looks like it was an effort and not at all like an error.

Fringe benefits

If your forehead is furrowed or has lines that bother you—try a fringe of bangs before you try a brow lift! Fringes of different lengths over the forehead can do wonders for your looks. Depending on your hair type, try to keep the bangs wispy and not too heavy, otherwise you run the risk of looking too severe. Think light and layered and your results will be kicky!

Playing the field

Rotating hair-care products keeps the hair fresher. We get bored with the same old, same old—so does our hair. By rotating, residue is not as likely to build up on the hair. Rotating products is an especially helpful technique to keep colored, permed, or otherwise processed hair at its best.

Dry run

If you need clean hair on the run with no time to wash, dry, and style, try "dry" cleaning. Talcum powder containing witch hazel, usually found in the drugstore, is an excellent quick fix for greasy hair. Put a small amount in the hands and gently rub the powder onto the scalp. Allow it to soak up the oils and debris for a couple of minutes. Then simply brush through thoroughly to remove. Witch hazel is an astringent and contains ingredients that help fight bacteria. Your scalp will feel cleansed, and your hair will feel much fresher and cleaner and will be easier to style.

Flake off

Maybe it's not dandruff. Then again, maybe it is. Who knows? Whatever it is, it just needs to flake off—somewhere else! If flakes are falling and it isn't the snow, try this remedy. Mix a few drops of rosemary oil with $\frac{1}{2}$ tablespoon of olive oil. Using your fingers rub well into the scalp at bedtime. Take a wide-tooth comb and gently comb from the scalp to only about one inch on the hair shaft. Cover head with a plastic, close-fitting shower cap. Allow the mixture to penetrate all night. In the morning shampoo and rinse thoroughly. Pat dry and style as usual. The rosemary oil is stimulating to the scalp, allowing the release of the dead, dry flakes. The olive oil is a wonderful natural moisturizer which helps soothe the scalp. Applying this remedy once or twice a month should give flakes the brush-off.

Fluff it up

To make the hair more voluminous, towel dry as completely as you can after washing the hair, then rub the hair closest to the roots between your fingers with a styling product. The rubbing action you should use is similar to what you would use to get pizza dough or a pie crust to stick to the edge of the pan: a bit of wiggling of the finger pads over the root area. This movement extends the hair at the root level, producing extra volume. To achieve that pump-up-the-volume look in between shampooing, rub a small bit of volumizing treatment onto dry hair while performing the rubbing technique. Your hair will speak volumes!

Fast defrizz

Frizzies can happen at any moment. For a 'do that won't do, tame the mane by breaking open a vitamin E capsule and rubbing the contents into your hands. Gently glide hands over frizzies to tame. Rub any leftover vitamin E oil into the finger cuticles to soften and hydrate them. Two treatments in one!

Part-on me

Ease the pain of a sun-burned scalp part with soothing green tea, as it is known to be a powerful anti-inflammatory. Make a cup of the green stuff and allow it to cool. Wash hair gently, being careful not to aggravate your painful scalp, and then massage the green tea into the scalp. Rinse lightly. The tea will not only ease the pain of sunburn, but add a healthy shine to the hair. Next time you plan to be out in the sun, remember your hat!

I'll have a cup of shine please

For hair that is ultra shiny, luxurious, and full of highlights, the rinse is as close as your kitchen. Cranberry juice brings out natural highlights for brunettes and redheads and gives a radiant and healthy shine. After shampooing and lightly conditioning, pour a cup of cranberry juice over the hair, making sure to work into the hair from the scalp to the ends. Then quickly rinse with a cup of cool water.

A cup of black coffee on dark brown or black hair is an excellent hair pick-me-up. First shampoo your hair and rinse. Next, lightly condition, and then rinse again. Pour on the cool coffee, work into the hair, and then give a final rinse with cool water. Your hair will look gorgeous!

Blonde hair can be highlighted by using a cup of chamomile tea followed by a cup of cool water. In all cases, shampoo and rinse, lightly condition, and rinse again before applying the tea. Wash out the tea, then pat dry and style as usual. Notice the wonderful shine—now that's everyone's cup of tea!

Brush on some gloss

For ultra shiny hair in three seconds flat, try this little trick. After you have styled your hair, spray some shine serum on a large, fluffy powder brush. Brush all over the hair and the shine will be like chrome! Be sure to dedicate the powder brush strictly to this new purpose since the ingredients in the hair product could wreak havoc on the skin.

Too much gunk

Greasy hair at the root? Dull, stiff, unstylable hair with split ends galore? The cause? Over processing via color, perms, styling, or all three. Take hair by the roots and take control of the situation. Shampoo only every other day with a normal hair type shampoo and really work it into the scalp. Rinse an extra time and use a tiny bit of conditioner on the ends. Once or twice a month, use a two to three minute conditioner to rehydrate the hair shaft. Over time your hair will show its gratefulness by looking and feeling wonderful.

Chapter 4

Tricks of the trade

If only once

If your budget permits, decide to splurge on a truly great, trendy, high-end salon for a consultation and cut. You can enjoy a "wealthy moment" long after the experience is over. When you arrive home, take photos to show your regular stylist so that they can keep the style maintained. When you tell your stylist all about the salon, the people, and what you saw, the stylist won't mind that you "cheated" on them. In fact, they will like maintaining the uptown 'do for you.

Last is best

When visiting a new stylist, call ahead to book a consultation first so that you can meet the stylist, discuss ideas, and allow them to see your hair. Try to book your appointment for the very end of the day. By having the last appointment, your stylist will not be rushed to get to the next client. You will have time to ask all of your questions, and the stylist will have time to answer them all. Now that's perfect planning!

Brush off

To keep hair and scalp looking and feeling their absolute best, proper care of any and all hair grooming tools must be a priority. Clean hair calls for clean brushes and combs, so remember to keep all hair-care items clean as a whistle by soaking them once a week in a solution of shampoo and water. Allow tools to soak for five minutes, rinse them carefully, and let them air dry. To really deep clean hair tools, put two capfuls of mouthwash or alcohol in a large water glass and soak for 15 minutes. Rinse and allow to dry naturally.

Product perfect

When deciding which hair products
to purchase, always read the labels
first, and ask your stylist for
advice. Products that may make
your hair look beautiful, could
actually be harmful to facial skin.
As we sleep, our heads go back
and forth on the pillow. Products
from the hair are released onto our
pillowcases every night—and then
transferred to our face when we toss and
turn. In this way, shampoos, hair moisturizers,
and styling products could actually wreak havoc on our
delicate facial skin. Everything needs to work in harmony.
Read the labels, ask the professionals, and preserve the skin.

Roll on

Curlers are now called rollers because we use them for much more than just curling the hair. We can add quick volume, height, waves, or even smooth the hair with a roller or two. After your hair is dry, roll a few rollers in the area that needs boosting, and spritz with hairspray. Leave in for a few minutes and remove. Style with your fingers and mist with hairspray. You are all set!

We knew it all along

A Yale University study on hair confirms what we ladies knew all along. Bad hair days are real and not just a figment of our imagination. According to the study, bad hair can have a very negative influence on self-esteem, causing people to concentrate on the worst aspects and features of their personality. Those who took part in the study felt that their social insecurities were heightened and their moods were, in general, communicated as unhappy or sad on those days when their hair felt out of control. In some cases, women even altered their plans to avoid being seen on those days. Bad hair, as if you didn't know, is hair that is overdue for a cut, color, or perm—hair that is overly frizzy, sticks out, or is wild, poofy, flyaway, bushy, greasy, flat, or just generally unruly. Just thinking about it is depressing. To keep bad hair days away from your door, at your next salon visit, ask your stylist for alternative ways to wear your hair. Having a hair plan "b" will work wonders for your mood—if you know ahead of time what to do. Hair that is subject to the frizzies, or the flyaways, or any (or all) of the above conditions needs taming to ensure that bad hair blues are banished!

Professional strength

Professional salon products are generally better than drugstore brands. Since salon brands are targeted to salon clients, who usually use more products on their hair than the average drugstore shopper, salon products have a lower pH level than inexpensive brands. They are kinder to the hair, and are more emollient than their less costly cousins. Better brands aid in removing products from the hair, as well as protecting the hair. If you color, perm, straighten, and the like, you cannot afford not to use professional products. Professional products have more active ingredients to keep the hair looking great, for longer.

Hot—not!

Keep water on the warm or slightly cool side—never hot—when washing your hair. Hot water dries the hair and the scalp—just like it dries the skin. Rinsing in too warm water will leave the hair cuticle open, allowing styling products to absorb into the hair, weighing it down. For the best 'do, keep it warm or cool it.

Photo op

When you finally have a hairstyle that you positively love, have a friend, or your spouse, take photos of your 'do from the front, side, and back on the day of your salon visit. Carefully look at the style and shape of the hair. Then tape the photos on your bathroom mirror. Each morning as you style you can see the exact look you are going for. Capturing the memory on film allows you to study the look and recreate it more easily.

Curly IQ

To roll a complete head of hair takes about 20 rollers, on average. How many of each sort you need is based on hair length and type, but a good measuring point is six each of four different sizes. If you are just spot curling your hair, you may want more of one or two different sizes in order to maximize curl.

See clearly

If you wear glasses, try to choose frames and a hairstyle that compliment each other. Large frames could spoil a neat, feathery cut, and very fine frames could be overpowered by a large, voluminous style.

Remember to take your glasses to the salon when having your hair restyled, so that the stylist can take the shape of the frames into consideration when deciding on an overall style.

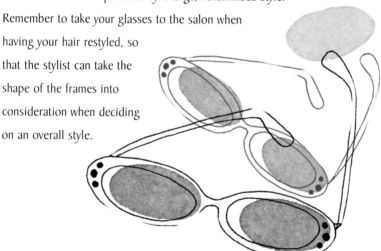

Roll up

To determine what different sized hair rollers you will need in your hair roller collection, measure the length of the hair that you want to lift on various sections of your head. You will need rollers with a diameter that is $^2/_3$ the length of the hair section being rolled. For example, if your hair is three inches long, choose a roller two inches across in circumference. If you are planning on curling four inches of hair then your roller size should be $2^3/_4$ inches around.

Out with the old

A shaft of hair has a life cycle of anywhere between two and seven years. When it is time for the hair to remove itself, strands of hair begin to drop out. Depending on your own hair cycle, at certain times you are apt to discover more hair than usual on your brush, your shoulders, your pillowcase, or caught in the shower drain. Stay calm and know that this is normal.

The older hair is being shed to make room for new re-growth. Even outside of the natural cycle of your hair, a healthy person loses about 100 hairs a day. Avoid excessive styling products, and brushing, so as not to aggravate hair loss. If your shedding of hair seems excessive, talk to your stylist about different products and remedies.

Times two

Balancing eyebrow color with hair color is critical to the success of an overall look. Dyed blonde hair paired with a set of dark eyebrows is never a good look! As a rule, for blonde hair, eyebrows should not go more than two shades darker than your hair color. Be sure to stick to the rule, otherwise instead of attracting admiring glances from strangers, you may start getting a few funny looks!

Heat control

Blow-dryers are wonderful tools. How did we ever manage without them?
Choose one that fits in your hand and allows you freedom of movement
without being too heavy.

Wattage should be kept to 1800. Anything
over that could dry the hair, causing it to
frizz, or worse, burn! The professional brands
often have multiple drying speeds so that you
can keep it on the cool side to finish and
seal the hair's cuticle.

On the wide side

Use a wide-tooth comb to spread conditioner evenly onto the hair. Wide-tooth combs are also great for curly hair, both wet and dry, as they don't get caught so easily in the curls. Opt for wooden or rubber combs every time if possible. Plastic combs can snag and tear the hair as well as increase flyaway ends. If plastic combs are the only choice available, keep flyaway hair to a minimum by putting a tiny amount of conditioner into a small spray bottle, fill the rest with water, and shake well. Before using the comb, spritz it with the conditioner mixture to help the hair lay in place and control those pesky flyaways.

Heavy metal

Metal hairbrushes are not to be used on your hair—period. The metal bristles will scratch the scalp and heat up too quickly when using with a blow-dyer, causing the hair to scorch or burn. Plus, using a metal styling tool will dramatically increase static electricity, causing dry, flyaway locks. Metal combs may even tear your hair and aggravate split ends. You certainly don't want damaged hair—so toss the metal gear aside and save your 'do.

Makeover moment

Professionals suggest scheduling a makeup makeover appointment if you have colored your hair differently. Your current lipstick, blusher, and eye shadow may not work any longer if you have changed your hair color to another hue. The makeup changes may only be subtle, but the end result of hair color and cosmetics being in perfect harmony is priceless.

Back on track

Even if you choose to color your hair at home, it is a good idea to have it professionally done every fifth or sixth coloring session. The home-care colors can vary from use to use as they are not as consistent as professional color. Plus your hair can be affected by your shampoo, conditioner, and styling products. A professional colorist will be able to judge how to correct and produce a perfect color. It is well worth the cost to factor in a professional colorist a few times a year.

Gray matters

Did you know that gray hair sometimes begins sneaking onto our scalps as early as our late teens! If a few gray hairs have begun to show up on your hair scene, you can disguise them with these easy tricks:

✳ Dark blonde or fine hair: try highlighting. The lighter streaks will hide the gray. Plus, since highlighting uses different tones, the effect will be very believable.

✳ Brunettes and redheads: try streaks of color for toning down the gray by streaking hair in darker, richer colors.

✳ Another option is color shampoos and color conditioners: these products add a hint of color and build up color with repeated use, helping cover the gray.

Chapter 5
Styling

Just plain lucky

Strong, shiny, soft tresses, full of life and body—styling is a breeze. This is just what normal hair enjoys. Having normal hair has as much to do with genetics as it does with eating a balanced diet and using the right products. If what you are doing is working, keep it up. Relish the fact that you are looking after your hair in the best way possible.

If you are still searching for "normal" hair—it may be as close as your kitchen. Eating a diet rich in protein, vitamins, and essential fatty acids will do wonders for your hair (and skin!). To be sure that you are getting all that your hair deserves, take a look at the skin, nail, and hair vitamins that are available at your health food store or pharmacy. Taken in addition to your regular multi-vitamin, these vitamins are formulated to supply just the right combination of nutrients to the skin, nails, and hair.

Brave heart

If you are up for a new 'do, and are game, call around to different hair salons and ask about their model nights. Model nights are when a teacher, or a visiting stylist educator, actually carries out the styling, cut and/or color while the new stylists and other team members observe. However, be careful as this is not always the case—sometimes an inexperienced pupil may be let loose on your hair, so be sure to ask who will handle the model night styling when making the appointment. Don't necessarily be put off if a junior has been booked to cut your hair. Sometimes it is the younger, less experienced stylists who come up with the freshest and most up-to-date styles. Weigh up the pros and cons—for a free style that is the latest in fashion, sometimes you just have to go for it!

Parting ways

Did you know that your hair part sends out signals about your personality? Who would have thought it?! But studies show that if you want to look more assertive and intelligent—locate your part on the extreme left side of your head. A part on the right side indicates you are a gentle and caring person. A center part says that you are trustworthy and dependable. Gosh, I wonder what a zigzag part says?

A cut above

A great hair cut moves with you. It's easy to style and looks good no matter what is going on. A great cut allows you to literally wash and go, should you desire to do so. How do you get a great cut? Talk to your stylist, communicate with photos, and listen to what the stylist says about your hair texture and what he or she thinks will work for you. If this doesn't work, keep an eye out for cute cuts on the heads of those around you. When you spot someone with a haircut that you just love, ask them where they get their hair done. Be sure to get their name as well as the stylist, so that when you are talking to the stylist about the great 'do, they will know whose 'do you mean.

Pump up the volume

If hair tends to be on the limp side, pump it up. Start off with a volumizing shampoo. A volumizing shampoo will be clean—not creamy. When washing, really concentrate on the scalp. Instead of a conditioner, which only weighs hair down, use a detangler product. Rinse, rinse, rinse. It cannot be said enough—rinse! Rinsing removes any extra styling goop or leftover shampoo that will make hair limp. Dry hair upside down so that the roots dry in the opposite direction to hair growth. This promotes extra volume and adds texture. Style and spray with a firm hold or extra hold hairspray, depending on your style.

Short stop

Short hair does not need conditioner. It makes the hair flat. If your hair is on the tangled side after shampooing, use a light cream rinse—not a conditioner—to rid the hair of tangles without weighing it down.

For shoulder length hair, opt for a lightweight, volumizing conditioner that will not weigh the hair down, but will condition gently.

Think it through

Before taking the plunge with a completely new 'do, ask and answer some very "stylish" questions. How much time do you have to style it? If you have stick-straight hair but crave curly, can you manage the maintenance of diffusing, curling, etc.? If you have curly locks but seek sleek hair, are you prepared to blow it straight each and every time you wash? After you ask and answer these questions, think of other changes that could affect your routine. After all has been asked—and you have arrived at your plan—do it!

Face it

Facial shape plays an important role when it comes to creating the best hairstyle for you. A good stylist works with your facial shape to create a flattering look that shows off your best features. To determine what kind of facial shape you have, take a photo of your face or find one in your photo album. Using a marker, draw around the outline of your face. Decide whether your shape is round, square, oval, or heart-shaped. Ask a friend her opinion as well. Once you have determined your facial shape, you are in great shape to find the perfect hairdo.

Banish the bouffant

If you suddenly glance in the mirror and notice that your hairstyle resembles a look from your old family photo album—don't panic! To calm down an overdone hairdo, put a scarf (preferably a silk scarf) around your hair, tying it at the neck for a few minutes. The scarf will de-puff the extra fluffy hair. In the case of severe over-puff, you might have to wear the scarf for a couple of extra minutes. The scarf trick is also perfect for adding additional sleekness to your style by smoothing down hair cuticles and giving you shiny hair without any extra styling time.

Short stories

To revive short hair and add volume, brush hair in the opposite direction from the way it is usually styled. Move the brush back and forth through the hair while bending over at the waist to add air. Stand upright. Lightly spray and voilà—instant volume!

If you know your party's extension, press star

Hair extensions are how the stars go from short hair to long hair, and back to short hair, seemingly overnight. Each hair extension is literally bonded to your real hair via heat for a look that is as natural as possible. Once the hair extensions are in place, you are free to wash, brush, and style your hair as you usually would. On average, extensions last up to four months, but can be removed at anytime should your style tastes change before then. On the negative side, extensions tend to be a bit pricey and can take a few hours to attach to the head, but how else can you grow your hair to any length desired in only one visit to the salon?

Fine print

The best length for fine hair is shoulder length or above. Longer styles with fine hair tend to look stringy and hair appears even thinner. Blunt cuts, wedge cuts, or even stacked layers work well with this hair type as the hair usually lays correctly. Moisturizing the hair is sometimes needed, but less is more, since fine hair can all of a sudden become flat and limp if too much extra conditioner is added.

Perms can really help to boost volume when styling fine hair, especially at the root or under layered sections to create a lift. To pump up the volume naturally try blow-drying the hair while bending at the waist, to lend movement and lightness to roots. Stop the drying process just before the hair is dry, and add a few Velcro rollers, spritz lightly with hairspray while you finish dressing to create hair that has even more bounce and body.

Volume up

Add instant volume to long hair by brushing the hair upside down with a large flat brush. Simply bend over at the waist and in long strokes, starting at the hair roots, brush downward toward the hair ends. Spray a bit of volumizer just on the roots and wait a few minutes for the product to dry (or click on the blow-dryer for a few seconds). Being careful not to bother the roots, just brush the tips of the hair, and flip hair back up—full of body and bounce. Va-va-voom!

Ban the bun

Longer hair can be worn with any facial shape provided that the style is current and face flattering. However, buns, as sleek and chic as they are on ballet dancers, can be too severe looking in the real world. Opt for layers and lightness if maintaining a longer mane. Upsweeps with some decorative chopsticks or hair ornaments are very stylish.

High styling

New on the styling scene are styling gels made with seaweed extracts. Marine products are well-known in the skin care area for their vitamin and mineral content. Recent discoveries show that the hair shaft also benefits from these treatments from the sea. In styling, the seaweed-based products help create shape and soft hold for all hair types, but especially for curly and wavy hair, by adding much needed shine.

Through thick and thin

Thick hair which is fine in texture, layers beautifully and has a lot of movement. A chin length or longer blunt cut will show off your thick, shiny hair. For a more contoured shape, try tapering gently around the face and bangs. Although hair is thick overall, it has the tendency to go flat or limp quickly because the individual hairs are fine. This hair type can benefit from a gentle perm. Highlighting the hair is also great to add body. Use gel at the roots and apply texturizer on the outer layers to get the most volume and fullness.

Curly clues

If your hair is coarse and curly, it is most likely to be dry, at least on the top layers. Since the hair bends and curls, shine is often missing from curly/wavy hair as well. To add shine, use a moisturizing conditioner to smooth the cuticle. At least once a week, use a deeper conditioner.

Gel makes styling easier. Apply all over wet hair. Let the hair dry naturally or use a diffuser to control curls. Scrunching is perfect to create a soft, tousled look. Layered cuts work best for this hair type. It is best to keep the layers on top a bit longer than the layers underneath to help reduce over-curling.

Flat out

To revive flat hair between shampooing, roll hair on Velcro rollers, mist ever so slightly with water, and put a large shower cap on top. Shower as usual. The steam from the shower will help set the style and give the hair extra volume. Blow-dry the rollers for just a minute or two until dry. Take the rollers out and va voom volume!

Stick straight

Straight hair is stronger than other hair types. However, straight hair is often resistant to color and to curling. Blunt cuts are great for this hair type. Feathering the hair at the edges and around the face is easy to do with straight hair. Straight hair typically enjoys a natural sheen and shine, since the hair cuticle is already smooth. A tiny bit of conditioner goes a long way. When blow-drying, a flat brush will create a straight blunt look, while a round brush will give the hair a more rounded edge.

Girls' night out

To add a bit of oomph, and instant glamour to your hair, roll it around Velcro rollers. Spray the rollers with an extra-hold hairspray and allow to set while applying your makeup. When you have completely finished dressing, remove rollers carefully, and run your fingers gently through your hair, creating a tousled, sexy look. Then simply spray with hairspray—and maybe even a spritz of perfume for added zing. Hair will smell gorgeous, look bouncy, and feel volumized—all ready for a night out on the tiles!

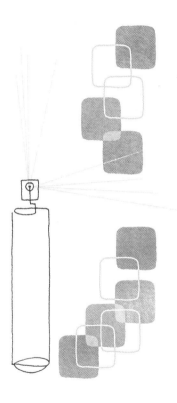

Susie Galvez

Armed with quick wit, years of professional experience, and more get-pretty tips than a beauty pageant coordinator, expert makeup artist, esthetician, and author Susie Galvez is dedicated to giving women tools to help them accept themselves and realize that each day is another chance to be beautiful.

Inspired by the thrill she gets from helping women rediscover beauty on a daily basis, Susie wrote the *Ooh La La! Effortless Beauty* series which includes *Ooh La La! Perfect Face*, *Ooh La La! Perfect Body*, *Ooh La La! Perfect Makeup*, and *Ooh La La! Perfect Hair*.

Susie is also the author of *Hello Beautiful: 365 Ways to Be Even More Beautiful*, *Weight Loss Wisdom: 365 Successful Dieting Tips*, and *InSPArations: Ideas, tips & techniques to increase employee loyalty, client satisfaction and bottom line spa profits*.

In addition to writing, Susie owns Face Works Day Spa in Richmond, Virginia. Face Works Day Spa has been featured in national and consumer magazines such as *Allure*, *Cosmopolitan*, *Elle*, and *Town and Country* as well as many

  **About the author**

trade publications including *Skin, Inc.*, *Dermascope*, *Day Spa*, *Salon Today*, *Nails Plus*, *Nails*, *Spa Management*, and *Les Nouvelles Esthetiques*. In April 2002, The Day Spa Association recognized Face Works as one of only 12 fully accredited day spas—out of 1,000 members—in the United States.

Susie is also recognized as one of the leading consultants in the spa industry, and is in high demand as a speaker at international spa conventions. She is a featured spokesperson for the beauty industry on radio and television programs, and is a member of Cosmetic Executive Women, The National Association of Women Business Owners, and the Society of American Cosmetic Chemists.

You can contact Susie at www.susiegalvez.com or by visiting her beauty website at www.beautyatyourfingertips.com, where you will find even more ways to have Ooh La La moments! Be sure to sign up for your free spa-at-home tips!

About the author

Special appreciation

"Follow your bliss." Joseph Campbell

This book could not have been completed without the unwavering support and love from my very special friends. Thank you for allowing me to follow my bliss:

Derrick Diggs for keeping me away from "bad hair days."

Audra Baca whose youthful spirit and turn of the word captured "me" on paper.

Dottie Dehart and Celia Rocks for their persistence in carrying my message out to the multitudes day after day.

Zaro Weil, friend and publisher, who entrusted me with her title.

To the superb concierge staff at Face Works Day Spa, who are responsible for creating perfect days for our clients, Amber Ensign, Spa Manager, and team members Laura Sereduik, Elleni Whitney, and Shannon Hutson.

And lastly, but always first with me, thank you Tino Galvez who is truly the wind beneath my wings.

XOXO